I Feel Bullied

Written by Jen Green
Illustrated by Mike Gordon

Kid-to-Kid Books

Red Set	Green Set	Blue Set	Yellow Set
I Feel Angry	I Feel Bored	I Feel Bullied	Excuse Me!
I Feel Happy	I Feel Jealous	I Feel Frightened	I Don't Care!
I Feel Lonely	I Feel Shy	I Feel Sad	I'll Do It!
It's Not Fair	I Feel Worried	Why Wash?	It Wasn't Me!

This edition published
in North America by
Sundance Publishing
P.O. Box 1326
234 Taylor Street
Littleton, MA 01460

First published in 1997 by
Wayland Publishers Limited

Copyright © 1997 Wayland Publishers Limited

ISBN 0-7608-4007-5

Printed in Canada

In the corner today,
we're talking about

feeling bullied.

This way to Kids Corner

3

When I feel bullied,

my tummy
ties itself in knots.

It's hard
to sleep at night.

I feel all alone, with no one to talk to.

I don't feel like eating.

5

When I feel bullied,
I feel hurt,
I feel frightened,
and I feel small.

But I tell my mom and dad,
and then I feel tall.

When a big kid chases me
and pulls my hair,
I feel bullied.

But I yell "OW!"
so everyone knows what's going on.

When other kids make fun
of my new glasses
and call me names,
I feel bullied.

But the teacher tells them to stop.

When my sister takes my toys
and breaks them,
I feel bullied.

But she's just upset
because our big brother
has been bullying her.

When mean kids in our neighborhood
make fun of my friend,
he feels bullied.

So he plays with me.
We have fun,
and he forgets about the bullies.

When my mom's boss yells at her, she feels bullied.

She feels better when she comes home.
Dad and I make dinner so she can relax.

When I feel bullied,
it helps to think about nice things
or something I am good at.

If I pretend I don't care,
the bully gives up and goes away.

Sometimes I feel brave enough
to stand up for myself.

I tell the bully to stop it.
Then I walk away.

Sometimes it's easier
to stand up for myself
if my friends are with me.

We let the bully know
that he can't scare us!

Sometimes talking to a bully helps.

Usually bullies are unhappy
or upset about something.
When they know someone cares,
they might feel better and be nicer.

Some grown-ups say,
"Hit the bully back."

Hit the
bully
back!

26

But hitting back can make things a lot worse.

If I can't stop the bullying myself,
I tell a grown-up.

What do you do
when you feel bullied?

Things to Do in the Kids Corner

List things you might be able to do if you were as tall as a tree. Compare your list with a friend.

Look through the book to find words with the double letters *ll, mm, tt, nn,* and *pp*.

Make up and draw a superhero. What special powers would your hero have? Draw a comic strip in which your hero helps someone who is being bullied.

Draw a picture of someone you think is brave. Give your picture to this person.

Ask a friend to be your "Bully Buddy." Together, think of things you can do to help each other if one of you is ever bullied. Write down your ideas and share them with other friends.

Other Books to Read

Bull Harris and the Purple Ooze, by Julie Mitchell (Sundance, 1997). Bull Harris is the meanest kid in my school. When he and his friends throw my school bag into a creek, do I tell on the class bully? *64 pages*

Bony-Legs, by Joanna Cole (Scholastic Books, 1983). A mean old witch bullies a young girl in this story based on a Russian fairy tale. *34 pages*

Molly's Pilgrim, by Barbara Cohen (Bantam, 1995). Molly and her family have moved to America to find freedom. But the kids in Molly's class make fun of Molly's accent and her clothes. *41 pages*

Cody and Quinn, Sitting in a Tree, by Kirby Larson (Dell, 1998). The fact that Quinn is a girl has never mattered to Cody. That is, until now, when that friendship becomes the focus of another classmate's bullying. *86 pages*

Farmer Duck, by Martin Waddell (Candlewick Press, 1996). A lazy farmer bullies a duck into working so hard that the duck almost collapses. But the other barnyard animals get together and chase the lazy farmer away. *30 pages*

Chrysanthemum, by Kevin Henkes (Morrow, 1996). Chrysanthemum thinks her name is absolutely perfect. But on the first day of school, classmates tease her about being named after a flower. Only Mrs. Delphinium Twinkle is able to make her blossom again. *32 pages*